Chatterbox

ENGLISH AS A SECOND LANGUAGE

Gillian Baxter
Hélène Bibeau

THIRD CYCLE, ELEMENTARY

ACTIVITY BOOK I

ANSWER KEY

ERPI
ÉDITIONS DU RENOUVEAU PÉDAGOGIQUE INC.

5757, RUE CYPIHOT
SAINT-LAURENT (QUÉBEC)
H4S 1R3

TÉLÉPHONE : (514) 334-2690
TÉLÉCOPIEUR : (514) 334-4720
COURRIEL : erpidlm@erpi.com

Project editor
Jocelyne Lauzière

Cover and book design
Tandem Conception et Infographie inc.

Illustrations
Chantale Audet: pages 83-88, 93, 95, 99; Danielle Bélanger: pages 1-38, 50-61, 66-82, 90-92, 94, 96-100, 101, 107, 108, 111; Anne-Marie Charest: pages 62-64; Dave Garneau: pages 39-43, 101, 108; Josée Masse: pages 113-122

428.24
·C437731
2003
Activity answer key

Dépôt légal : 2ᵉ trimestre 2003
Bibliothèque nationale du Québec
National Library of Canada
Imprimé au Canada

ISBN 2-7613-1341-0
1234567890   HLN   09876543
10532 ABCD   0F10

Contents

Message to the Teacher

This full-colour Activity Book accompanies Student's Book 1 of the Chatterbox series for the third cycle. It replaces most of the reproducible handouts provided in the Teacher's Guide, thus relieving teachers of the time-consuming task of making photocopies. All instructions are written in clear, simple language, and the number of pictograms has been kept to a minimum to avoid confusion.

Activity Book 1 provides material to accompany the warm-up, the activities and the wrap-up of each unit of Student's Book 1. The Activity Book also contains one or more extension activities in each unit that can be used for remediation or enrichment, in class or at home. In addition, each unit ends with one and sometimes two extra activities that can be used for a variety of purposes.

Pictograms

 This indicates the corresponding page in the Student's Book.

 This section contains a questionnaire for student self-evaluation.

We hope you enjoy using Chatterbox and wish you a successful school year.

Chers parents,

Le but du cours d'anglais au primaire est de permettre aux enfants d'acquérir une connaissance fonctionnelle de la langue seconde. Ainsi, dès le premier jour de classe, votre enfant commencera à acquérir le vocabulaire de base et les stratégies d'apprentissage qui lui permettront d'échanger avec ses camarades de classe en anglais. Durant l'année scolaire, votre enfant sera appelé à participer à diverses activités qui visent surtout à développer la communication orale.

Le présent cahier soutient et renforce les activités du manuel de l'élève; il propose également des activités d'enrichissement en lien avec les thèmes abordés en classe. À la fin de chaque activité, de même qu'à la fin de chaque unité, votre enfant aura l'occasion de faire le point sur ses apprentissages à l'aide d'un questionnaire d'auto-évaluation. Nous vous encourageons à consulter régulièrement ces pistes d'évaluation afin de suivre le cheminement de votre enfant.

L'enseignante ou l'enseignant de votre enfant vous proposera des moyens pour poursuivre et consolider l'apprentissage de l'anglais à la maison. Parmi ces moyens, il y a en un qui nous semble plus important que les autres. Ce moyen, c'est de valoriser les efforts de votre enfant dans la langue seconde. L'importance que votre enfant accordera à l'apprentissage de l'anglais dépendra dans une large mesure de l'importance que vous y accorderez.

Recevez, chers parents, nos meilleures salutations.

Les auteures de Chatterbox,

Gillian Baxter

Hélène Bibeau

All about Me!

Name: _____

Age: _____

Group: _____

Glue your photo here.

Favourite animal: _____

Favourite book: _____

Favourite cartoon character: _____

Favourite colour: _____

Favourite game: _____

Favourite meal: _____

Favourite pastime: _____

Favourite snack: _____

Favourite treat: _____

Favourite TV program: _____

Favourite Web site: _____

Unit 1

That Looks Familiar!

 Warm-up

What Do You Remember?

► Write the names of all the objects in the picture.

pencil

eraser

book

computer

marker

ball, basketball

glue stick, glue

scissors

paper, notebook

- **I named all the objects in the picture.** Yes ☐ No ☐
- **I remembered _____ words that I learned last year.**

Unit 1

Activity 1 This Is Me

► **Complete the identification form.**

Personal Identification

Name: _____

Age: _____

Address: _____

Telephone: _____

Favourite food: _____

Favourite sports: _____

Favourite subjects: _____

Family members: _____

_____

Students will fill in their own personal identification form.

- **I completed the form.**   Yes ☐   No ☐
- **I helped my partner.**   Yes ☐   No ☐
- **I corrected my work.**   Yes ☐   No ☐

That Looks Familiar!   three **3**

Activity **2** I Know That Word!

▶ **Make a list of ten English words you know.**
▶ **Illustrate the words.**

Answers will vary. _____   _____

_____   _____   _____   _____

_____   _____   _____

- **My list had _____ words.**
- **My group made a list of _____ words.**
- **I used Chatterbox 11 for help.**   Yes ☐   No ☐

Is That English?

► **Identify four different types of English words.**

identical
similar
tricky
different

Answers: (1) identical: look the same, mean the same; (2) similar: look the same, mean the same, a few letters are different; (3) tricky: identical or similar, mean something different; (4) different.

► **Look at the pages in this unit.**
► **Find eight words that are identical or similar to French words.**

Identical

Possible answers: restaurant, lion, orange, zoo, garage, pizza, page, pure

Similar

Possible answers: blue, cereal, to observe, to complete, familiar, similar, identical, letter, activity, juice, soup, cream, tomato

---

- **The text was:**
  Very easy ☐   Easy ☐   Difficult ☐   Very difficult ☐
- **In this unit, I found _____ words that are similar or identical to French words.**
- **I know the meaning of these words.**
  All of them ☐   Most of them ☐   Some of them ☐   None of them ☐

That Looks Familiar!   five **5**

Extension Activity

More Familiar Friends

► Look through your book.
► Find more words that are identical or similar to French words.

Students will write their words on or around the picture for each unit.

Unit 2

Unit 4

Unit 3

Unit 5

Unit 6

Unit 7

Unit 8

Unit 9

Unit 10

Unit 11

Unit 12

That Looks Familiar!

Activity 4 English All around Me

▶ **Find English words around you.**

▶ **Complete the chart.**

WORDS ALL AROUND ME		
WORD	WHAT IT MEANS	WHERE I SAW IT
pizza		*pizza box*
Students will complete the chart with the English words they find in their surroundings.		

- **I found _____ English words around me.**
- **I found these words in _____ places.**

► **Plan the front cover of your Learner's Logbook.**

Name: _____

Learner's Logbook for English

Students will plan the front covers of their logbooks.

• **I am satisfied with my Learner's Logbook.**   Yes ☐   No ☐
• **I worked hard during this unit.**
  Always ☐   Most of the time ☐   Some of the time ☐   Never ☐

Reflecting on Words

Look at the words below. Do you recognize them?
Are they identical or similar to English words?

► Write the English word for each.
► Check your dictionary
for the correct spelling.

1.	architecture	*architecture*
2.	astronaute	*astronaut*
3.	automne	*autumn*
4.	barbecue	*barbecue*
5.	civilisation	*civilization*
6.	docteur	*doctor*
7.	éducation	*education*
8.	géographie	*geography*
9.	poème	*poem*
10.	universel	*universal*

Unit 2

Secrets from the Tomb

Warm-up

What Do You Know?

▶ **Write words about Ancient Egypt.**

_____

Ancient Egypt

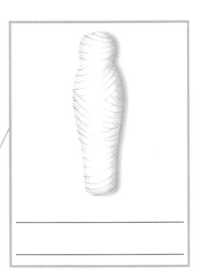

_____

_____

_____

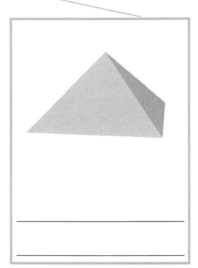

_____

Possible answers: tomb, mummy, god, goddess, Anubis, temple, tomb, burial, papyrus, Nile, writing, communication, hieroglyphics, pharaoh, Tutankhamen, ruler.

I shared my ideas with my classmates.
Always ☐   Most of the time ☐   Some of the time ☐   Never ☐

I used Chatterbox 4 for help.   Yes ☐   No ☐

My group found _____ words about Ancient Egypt.

Activity 1 — Into the Tomb

▶ Draw a line from each object to the room where it was found.

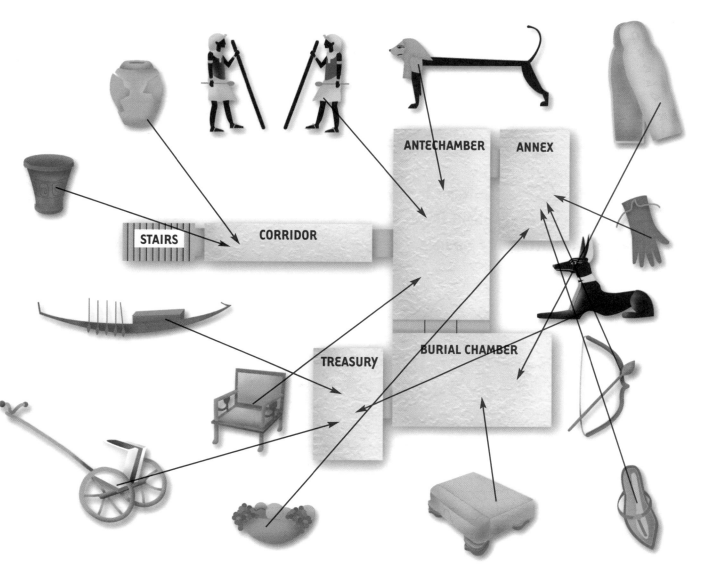

STAIRS
CORRIDOR
ANTECHAMBER
ANNEX
TREASURY
BURIAL CHAMBER

I understood the key words in the newspaper clipping.   Yes ☐   No ☐

Secrets from the Tomb

Activity 2 — This Is My Life

► **List five things to include in your pyramid.**

> *Students will name five things they would include in their pyramid.*

- I chose _____ items for my pyramid.
- I told my partner about them.   Yes ☐   No ☐
- I used Chatterbox 2 for help.   Yes ☐   No ☐

Activity 3 — Ruler for a Day

1. *Students will write five rules for their classroom.*

2. _____

3. _____

4. _____

5. _____

_____
Signature

- **I understood the text in Hatshepsut's diary.**

  All of it ☐   Most of it ☐   Some of it ☐   None of it ☐

Activity 4 Written in Stone

▶ **Decode the hieroglyphics.**

T u t a n k h a m e n

1 mummy

2 king

3 Egypt

4 stone

5 tomb

6 Rosetta

7 hieroglyphics

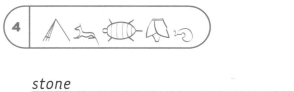

- **I was able to decode the hieroglyphics.**

  All of them ☐   Most of them ☐   Some of them ☐   None of them ☐

- **I decoded the hieroglyphics with ☐ or without ☐ help.**

Special Symbols

▶ **Read the text.**

Egyptian hieroglyphics did not have vowels. Egyptians used only consonants to write their words. Sometimes it was difficult to understand the meaning of a particular word. For example, the words "parrot" and "pirate" were written the same way:

To help people understand the meaning of a particular word, Egyptians included a special hieroglyph called a "determinative." For "parrot" they probably drew a bird and for "pirate" they probably drew a pirate ship.

▶ **Find the meaning of the words.**
▶ **Invent a determinative for them.**

fort

Students will draw a castle or tower.

ferret

Students will draw a ferret.

Wrap-up

▶ **Write the texts for your pyramid book.**

Students will write the rough copies of their texts.

I think my pyramid book is_____

_____.

I am satisfied with my work.

Extremely ☐   Very ☐   Not very ☐   Not at all ☐

Secrets from the Tomb

Figure It Out!

▶ **Write a message, using hieroglyphics.**
▶ **Give it to a friend.**
▶ **See if your friend can figure it out.**

My secret message

Students will write a message, using hieroglyphics.

_____

_____

_____

I figured it out!   **Signature:** _____

Unit 3

Every Drop Counts

Warm-up

What Do You Know?

▶ **Identify how we use water.**

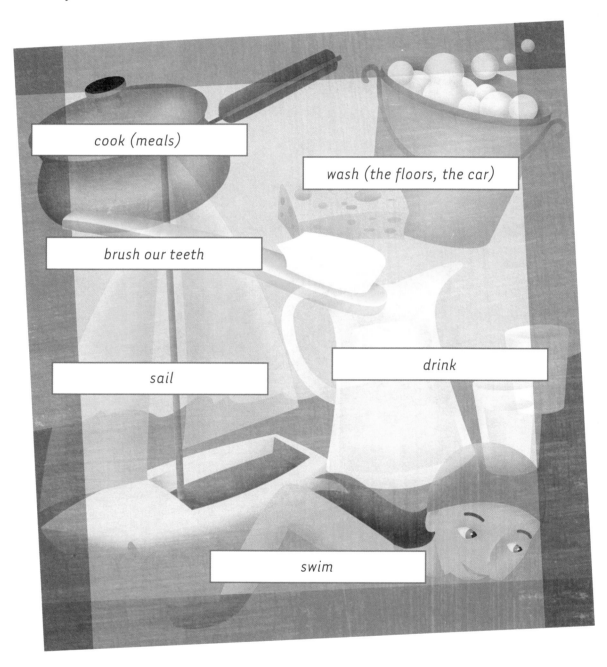

cook (meals)

wash (the floors, the car)

brush our teeth

sail

drink

swim

- **I identified** _____ **ways to use water.**

Activity 1

How the Fly Saved the River

▶ **Answer the following questions.**

1. Who created the problem? _a moose_

2. What did he do? _He drank too much water from the river._

3. How did the other animals feel? _They were worried._

4. What did the animals say? _____

    The beavers said: _"Our homes will be destroyed."_

    The deer and the foxes said: _"What will we drink if the water disappears?"_

    The fish said: _"Our homes will be destroyed, and we cannot live on the land."_

5. Who solved the problem? _a small black fly_

6. What did she do? _She bit the moose again and again._

▶ **Look at the illustrations in your book.**
▶ **Place the sentences in the appropriate order.**

A. The fly bit the moose again and again.   _7_

B. All the animals wanted the moose to leave.   _5_

C. Many years ago there was a beautiful river.   _1_

D. The fly was very proud of herself.   _9_

E. All the animals were worried.   _4_

F. One day a moose came to the river to drink some water.   _2_

G. A small black fly offered to make the moose leave.   _6_

H. The water started to sink lower and lower.   _3_

I. The moose ran away from the pesky fly.   _8_

- **I understood the problem in the story.**   Yes ☐ No ☐
- **I discovered why the animals were worried.**   Yes ☐ No ☐
- **I placed the sentences in order with ☐ or without ☐ help.**

Activity 2 — How Much Water Do You Use?

SB 25-26

► **Interview each member of your household.**
► **Find out how much water he or she uses a week.**

Example: 4 times/day x 7 days/week = 28 times/week x 20 litres = **560** litres/week

Answers will vary.

Indoor Activities

Name:				
How many times a day do you . . .	/day	x 7 = /week	x litres	Total
flush the toilet?		x 7 =	x 20	
take a shower?		x 7 =	x 100	
take a bath?		x 7 =	x 150	
brush your teeth?		x 7 =	x 10	
Total:				litres/week

Name:				
How many times a day do you . . .	/day	x 7 = /week	x litres	Total
flush the toilet?		x 7 =	x 20	
take a shower?		x 7 =	x 100	
take a bath?		x 7 =	x 150	
brush your teeth?		x 7 =	x 10	
Total:				litres/week

- **I interviewed members of my household.** Yes ☐ No ☐
- **I calculated my family's water consumption.** Yes ☐ No ☐
- **I used Chatterbox 6 for help.** Yes ☐ No ☐

Continued on next page

22 twenty-two

Unit 3

▶ **Interview your parents or guardian.**
▶ **Find out how much water your household uses every week.**

Example: 11 times/week x 20 litres = 220 litres/week

Answers will vary.

Indoor Activities

How many times a week do we . . .	/day	x 7 =	/week	x litres	Total
wash the dishes by hand?		x 7 =		x 35	
use the dishwasher?		x 7 =		x 40	
cook food?		x 7 =		x 20	
use the washing machine?		x 7 =		x 225	
clean the house?		x 7 =		x 75	
Total:					litres/week

Outdoor Activities

How many times a week do we . . .	/day	x 7 =	/week	x litres	Total
wash the car?		x 7 =		x 400	
clean the driveway?		x 7 =		x 250	
How many minutes a week do we water the yard and garden?			x 35 litres/min		
Total:					litres/week

▶ **Calculate how much water your family uses indoors and outdoors every week.**
▶ **Add up all the totals.**

Example: 1460 + 1680 + 1550 + 2030 + 2990 + 2500 = 12 210

Conclusion: Every week my family uses a grand total of _____ litres of water indoors and outdoors.

Activity **3**

Save It, Don't Waste It

SB 27

► **Match each card with the appropriate person.**
► **Write the letters on the blank lines.**

A. I take a shower that lasts only six minutes.	D. I fill up the dishwasher and use it once a day.
B. I brush my teeth four times a day. I leave the water running while I brush.	E. I brush my teeth four times a day. I turn off the tap while I brush.
C. I fill my bath with as much water as possible.	F. I wash the dishes by hand three times a day. I rinse the dishes under running water.

Sally Saver

A _____
D _____
E _____

Wally Waster

B _____
C _____
F _____

- **I was able to match each card with the appropriate person.** Yes ☐ No ☐
- **I spoke English with my partner.**
  Always ☐   Most of the time ☐   Some of the time ☐   Never ☐
- **I used Chatterbox 11 for help.**   Yes ☐ No ☐

Don't Forget!

► **Write some reminders for your family.**
► **Include a slogan and a water-saving tip.**

Save a fish!
A toilet is not
a garbage can.

_____
_____
_____
_____
_____
_____

_____
_____
_____
_____
_____

_____
_____
_____
_____
_____

Students will write a slogan and a water-saving tip on each piece of note paper.

Activity 4 Drip, Drip, Drip

▶ **Complete the sentences.**

1. Use a water-saving shower head and save _____30_____ litres of water every time you take a shower.

2. Use a faucet aerator and save_____5_____ litres of water every minute you let the water run.

3. Fix all leaky taps. A drop a second fills a_____25-litre_____ bucket in one day.

4. Fix all leaky toilets and save up to _____100_____ litres a day.

5. Use a soaker hose. You can save about_____1000_____ litres every hour.

6. Get a rain barrel and collect rain water. You can fill a_____9-litre_____ watering can twenty times.

Use water-saving shower heads and faucet aerators.

Fix all tap and toilet leaks.

Use a soaker hose.

Use a rain barrel.

• **I identified the amounts of water that can be saved.**
  All of them ☐   Most of them ☐   Some of them ☐   None of them ☐

Wrap-up

▶ **Plan your skit.**

▶ Present a situation that wastes water.

_____

_____

▶ Write the dialogue.

_____

_____

_____

_____

▶ Explain how much water is used.

_____

_____

▶ Write the dialogue.

_____

_____

_____

_____

▶ Suggest one solution to the problem.

_____

_____

▶ Write the dialogue.

_____

_____

_____

_____

▶ Invent a water-saving slogan.

_____

_____

▶ Write the dialogue.

_____

_____

_____

_____

Students will write a rough draft of their skits.

- **I prepared a skit with my partners.**　　　　　Yes ☐　No ☐
- **I worked:**
  Very hard ☐　Moderately hard ☐　Not very hard ☐　Not hard at all ☐
- **I spoke English.**
  Always ☐　　Most of the time ☐　　Some of the time ☐　　Never ☐

Test Your Knowledge about Fresh Water

▶ **Fill in the blanks with the correct answers.**

1. Fresh water represents about _____ percent of the world's water.	**③** 9	15
2. Canada has nearly_____ percent of all the fresh water in the world.	10 **㉠**	40
3. Nearly_____ of the world's fresh water is found underground.	$\frac{1}{3}$ $\frac{1}{2}$	**$\frac{2}{3}$**
4. Each Canadian uses about_____ litres of water a day inside and outside the home.	200 **㉟⓪**	500
5. About _____ percent of all water consumption in a home occurs in the bathroom.	45 55	**㊕**
6. During the summer, _____ percent of water used in a household is used outside.	25 33	**㊿**
7. Drinking water represents about_____ percent of all municipal water.	**③** 15	40
8. Around _____ percent of all municipal water is lost before it reaches its final destination.	7 **⑭**	21
9. Each household that adopts water-saving practices can reduce its water consumption by_____ percent.	20 30	**㊵**
10. Around the world approximately_____ people die every day of diseases caused by unclean water.	20 000 **(34 000)** 75 000

How did you score?

Ask your teacher to correct your test. Write your score: _____ .
Read the statement that applies to you.

8–10   Wow! You know how important fresh water is. You will certainly leave some for your grandchildren!

5–7   Not bad! Discover more ways to save fresh water. You'll see that it's not difficult.

0–4   Watch out! You need to learn a lot more about fresh water. You'll see how important it is.

Unit 4

Sweet Tooth

Warm-up

Yummy Treats!

► Name some treats we can make with chocolate.

► Name some of the different ways we can eat ice cream.

_____

_____

_____

_____

_____

_____

_____

_____

_____

_____

Possible answers: chocolate milk, chocolate bar, chocolate fondue, chocolate sauce, chocolate Easter bunny/rabbit, chocolate candies, brownies / ice cream cone, ice cream sundae, ice cream bar, ice cream cake, banana split, milkshake

- I identified _____ treats we can make with chocolate.
- I named my favourite treat. Yes ☐ No ☐

Activity 1 Everybody Likes a Treat

► **Find out what treats your classmates like.**

Question	Answer	Student's name
1. What's your favourite ice cream?		
2. What's your favourite chocolate bar?		

Students will ask their classmates the two questions and write down their answers.

- **I worked well with my partner.**   Yes ☐   No ☐
- **My partner and I interviewed** _____ **classmates.**
- **I used Chatterbox 11 for help.**   Yes ☐   No ☐

Sweet Tooth

Activity 2 Did You Know?

▶ **Write a fact about chocolate in each square.**

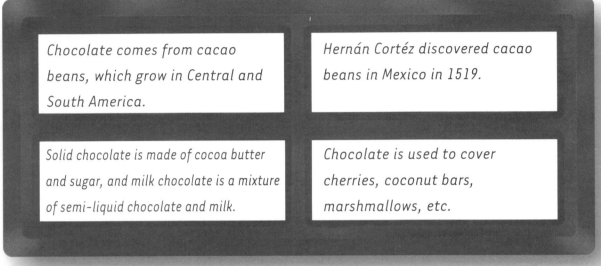

Chocolate comes from cacao beans, which grow in Central and South America.

Hernán Cortéz discovered cacao beans in Mexico in 1519.

Solid chocolate is made of cocoa butter and sugar, and milk chocolate is a mixture of semi-liquid chocolate and milk.

Chocolate is used to cover cherries, coconut bars, marshmallows, etc.

Students will write one fact about chocolate after listening to the recording.

▶ **Write some facts about ice cream.**

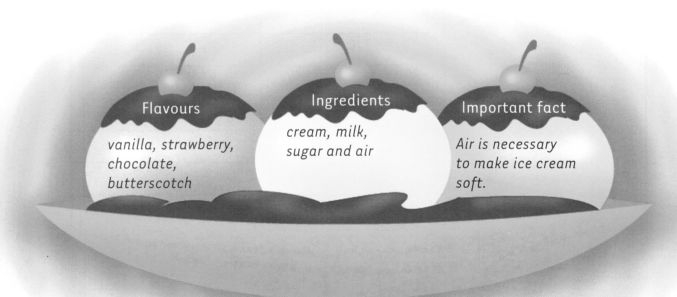

Flavours

vanilla, strawberry, chocolate, butterscotch

Ingredients

cream, milk, sugar and air

Important fact

Air is necessary to make ice cream soft.

- **The listening text on chocolate was:**
  Very easy ☐   Easy ☐   Difficult ☐   Very difficult ☐
- **The reading text on ice cream was:**
  Very easy ☐   Easy ☐   Difficult ☐   Very difficult ☐

Activity 3 Going Bananas

▶ **Read the recipes.**
▶ **Match each recipe with an illustration.**

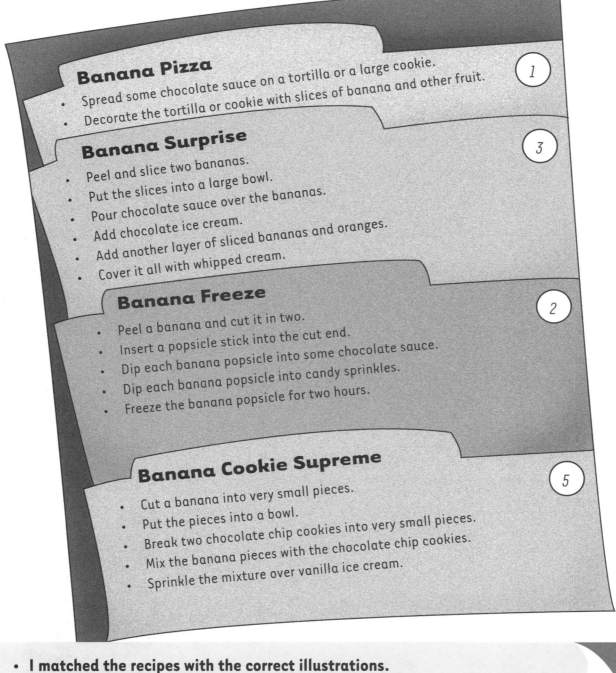

Banana Pizza
- Spread some chocolate sauce on a tortilla or a large cookie.
- Decorate the tortilla or cookie with slices of banana and other fruit.

1

Banana Surprise
- Peel and slice two bananas.
- Put the slices into a large bowl.
- Pour chocolate sauce over the bananas.
- Add chocolate ice cream.
- Add another layer of sliced bananas and oranges.
- Cover it all with whipped cream.

3

Banana Freeze
- Peel a banana and cut it in two.
- Insert a popsicle stick into the cut end.
- Dip each banana popsicle into some chocolate sauce.
- Dip each banana popsicle into candy sprinkles.
- Freeze the banana popsicle for two hours.

2

Banana Cookie Supreme
- Cut a banana into very small pieces.
- Put the pieces into a bowl.
- Break two chocolate chip cookies into very small pieces.
- Mix the banana pieces with the chocolate chip cookies.
- Sprinkle the mixture over vanilla ice cream.

5

- **I matched the recipes with the correct illustrations.**
  All four recipes ☐   Three recipes ☐   Two recipes ☐   One recipe ☐
- **I wrote my own recipe following the models.**   Yes ☐   No ☐

Sweet Tooth

Fruity Treats

► **Rewrite two of the recipes, using another fruit.**

► **Give each recipe a name.**

Students will rewrite two recipes and give them a new name.

Activity 4 Taste Test

▶ **Interview your partner.**
▶ **Check off your partner's answers.**

Name of dessert	Sweet	Crunchy	Smooth	Delicious
1.				
2.				
3.				
4.				
5.				

Students will interview their partners and check off their answers.

- **I spoke English with my partner.**
  Always ☐   Most of the time ☐   Some of the time ☐   Never ☐
- **I described the taste of** _____ **desserts.**

Sweet Tooth

Wrap-up

▶ **Plan your special treat.**

Answers will vary.

Ingredients

_____

_____

_____

_____

Description

_____

_____

_____

_____

Sketch

- **I am satisfied with the treat I invented.**
  Extremely ☐　　　Very ☐　　　Not very ☐　　　Not at all ☐

- **I checked my work carefully.**　　　Yes ☐　No ☐

- **I followed the model in the book.**　　Yes ☐　No ☐

Party Time

▶ **Make a menu for a Sweet-Tooth Party.**
▶ **Write the treats you would serve at your party.**
▶ **Draw a picture of your treats.**

Answers will vary.

_____

_____

_____

_____

_____

Sweet-Tooth Party

Puzzle Treats

► **Solve the puzzles.**
► **Write one letter in each box.**

1. This fruit is small and red. | c | h | e | r | r | y |

2. This drink is made with ice cream and milk.
| m | i | l | k | s | h | a | k | e |

3. This fruit is long and yellow. | b | a | n | a | n | a |

4. To make a Banana Surprise, I followed a | r | e | c | i | p | e | .

5. Frozen milk, cream and air make | i | c | e | c | r | e | a | m | .

6. Peanuts are | c | r | u | n | c | h | y | .

7. I like the | t | a | s | t | e | of chocolate.

8. My | f | a | v | o | u | r | i | t | e | kind of ice cream is strawberry.

9. Chocolate and | v | a | n | i | l | l | a | are two flavours of ice cream.

10. Chocolates and ice cream are delicious | t | r | e | a | t | s | .

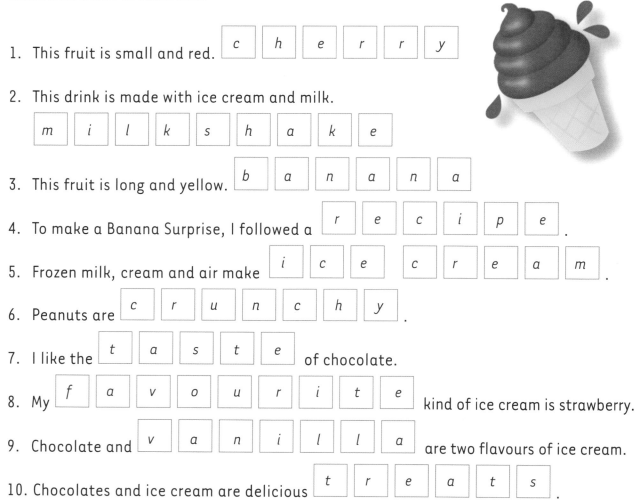

Unit 5

The Night of Giving

My Bookmark

▶ **Complete the first two sentences on your bookmark.**

The title of the story is
The Night of Giving .

I think the story is about
Students will predict what they think the story is about. .

Why are the children frightened?
The children are frightened because the village of
Sansson-de-Rire is a dirty and unhappy place. .

What is Muron's plan?
Muron's plan is to visit Sansson-de-Rire on the
Night of Giving. .

What do you think is going to happen?
Students will write what they think is going to
happen next. .

My prediction was *correct / incorrect* .
I liked ☐ **didn't like** ☐ **this story because**

Students will state whether their predictions were
right or wrong. They will explain why they did or did
not like the story. .

• **I completed the first two sentences on my bookmark.**   Yes ☐ No ☐

Activity 1 The Children of Kelm

▶ **Write the names of the characters.**

Muron
_____

Shan
_____

El
_____

adults of Kelm
_____

stranger
_____

• **I can identify the characters in the story.**
All of them ☐ Most of them ☐ Some of them ☐ None of them ☐

Activity 2 A Year of Sadness

► **Write about the children's problems.**

There were no parents to:

- help
- make phone calls
- drive them around
- look up information
- find things
- cook meals
- hug and kiss them
- fix things

- **I identified the children's problems.**   Yes ☐ No ☐
  All of them ☐   Most of them ☐   Some of them ☐   None of them ☐
- **I used Chatterbox 2 for help.**   Yes ☐ No ☐

Activity 3

A New Discovery

Where and when?

Kelm and Sansson-de-Rire

The Night of Giving

- **I can name the two villages where the story takes place.** Yes ☐ No ☐
- **I completed the second section on my bookmark.** Yes ☐ No ☐
- **I used Chatterbox 6 for help.** Yes ☐ No ☐

Activity 4

Thank You for Giving

What I learned

Sharing makes us all happy.

- **I completed the last two sentences on my bookmark.** Yes ☐ No ☐
- **I agree with the message of the story.** Yes ☐ No ☐
- **The story was easy to read.** Yes ☐ No ☐
- **This story made me feel** _____ .

Before and After

► **Draw two pictures of Sansson-de-Rire.**
► **First draw what the children expected to see.**
► **Then draw what they actually saw.**

What the children expected to see:

Students should draw a dirty village with grey houses, brown grass and dark streets. There are no flowers. There is nowhere for children to play.

What the children saw:

Students should draw a village with decorated houses. They should draw pine logs in the fireplaces of the houses and pumpkin pies in the kitchens. There are flowers in the gardens and a park with swings and slides.

Wrap-up

▶ **Plan what you will write on your gift certificates.**

Gift Certificate

To: _____

Students will write rough drafts of their
gift certificates.

From: _____

Gift Certificate

To: _____

_____

_____

From: _____

Gift Certificate

To: _____

_____

_____

From: _____

Gift Certificate

To: _____

_____

_____

From: _____

- **I made giving bags and gift certificates for:**

_____

_____ .

- **When I gave** _____ **a gift certificate,** _____
                   (name)   (he or she)

_____ .

The Night of Giving

Celebrations of Giving

▶ **Find the hidden words.**
▶ **Discover the mystery message.**

Birthday	Father's Day	Mother's Day	Ramadan
Christmas	Hanukkah	New Year's Day	Shichi-Go-San
Diwali	Id-ul-Fitr	Pesach	St. Valentine
Easter	Kwanzaa	Purim	Thanksgiving

N	A	S	O	G	I	H	C	I	H	S	G
H	S	T	V	A	L	E	N	T	I	N	E
A	B	M	E	A	S	T	E	R	I	E	Y
N	I	H	A	Z	K	E	M	V	D	W	A
U	R	N	C	N	E	V	I	E	U	Y	D
K	T	A	R	A	Y	G	R	D	L	E	S
K	H	D	A	W	S	Y	U	A	F	A	R
A	D	A	G	K	I	E	P	V	I	R	E
H	A	M	N	I	N	G	P	D	T	S	H
A	Y	A	D	I	W	A	L	I	R	D	T
C	H	R	I	S	T	M	A	S	Y	A	O
T	F	A	T	H	E	R	S	D	A	Y	M

▶ **What is the mystery message?**

Make every day a giving day. __ __ __ __ __ __ __ __ __ __ __ __ __ __

▶ **Why don't you find out more about these celebrations of giving?**

Unit
6

Monsters: Real or Fake?

Real or Fake?

► Look at the pictures of the monsters.
► Check off your opinions.

	My opinion		
	I think it's real.	I'm not sure.	I think it's fake.
1.	*Answers: Real = 1, 2 and 3; fake = 4; unproven =5*		
2.			
3.			
4.			
5.			

• I gave my opinion about the monsters.	Yes ☐	No ☐
• I used Chatterbox 6 for help.	Yes ☐	No ☐

Activity 1 Where Are They Hiding?

▶ **Identify where the monsters usually hide.**

1. **Lake monsters hide** _in large, deep, cold lakes._

2. **Sea monsters hide** _at the bottom of the Atlantic and Pacific Oceans._

3. **Mountain monsters hide** _in mountains and forests._

▶ **Complete the chart.**
▶ **Identify the creatures and the places where people have seen them.**

Creatures	Places
Nessie	Loch Ness, Scotland
Ogopogo	Okanagan Lake, Canada
Memphré	Lake Memphrémagog, Québec
sea serpents	Atlantic and Pacific Oceans
the kraken	Atlantic and Pacific Oceans
yeti	Himalayas
Bigfoot	United States
the sasquatch	Northwestern North America

- • **I found the most important information in the texts that I read.**
  All of it ☐   Most of it ☐   Some of it ☐   None of it ☐
- • **I used Chatterbox 8 for help.**   Yes ☐   No ☐

Monsters: Real or Fake?

Activity 2 I Saw...

▶ **Get ready to listen to the reports.**

▶ **Answer the questions about the monsters.**

1. Which monster weighs 250 kg? _____*Number 7*_____

2. Which monster has three small humps? _____*Number 2*_____

3. Which monster is 15 metres long? _____*Number 11*_____

4. Which monster has ten legs that are each 12 metres long? _____*Number 13*_____

5. Which monster has a footprint that is 50 cm long? _____*Number 9*_____

▶ **Listen to the reports.**

▶ **Write the number of the monster described in each report.**

Report 1: _____*Number 4*_____

Report 2: _____*Number 6*_____

Report 3: _____*Number 8*_____

Report 4: _____*Number 11*_____

Report 5: _____*Number 12*_____

- **I identified the monsters described in the reports.**
  All of them ☐   Most of them ☐   Some of them ☐   None of them ☐

Activity 3 — What Makes a Monster a Monster?

► **Complete the cards about the monsters.**

Name: King Kong

Animal: *gorilla*

Size: *giant*

Measurements: *8 metres*

Special powers: *strong, aggressive*

Name: Godzilla

Animal: *lizard*

Size: *huge*

Measurements: *50 metres, 20 tonnes*

Special powers: *strong, radioactive breath*

Name: Ghidrah

Animal: *flying reptile*

Size: *enormous*

Measurements: *100 metres, 30 tonnes, wingspan of 150 metres*

Special body parts: *3 heads, 2 tails*

Special powers: *fiery breath*

Name: Velociraptor

Size: *enormous*

Measurements: *4-5 metres, 300 kg*

Special body parts: *sharp teeth, long claws*

► **Complete the sentence.**
The monster that scares me the most is _____ *Answers will vary.* .

- I identified the characteristics of famous movie monsters.   Yes ☐ No ☐
- I made a list of animals that could be transformed into monsters.   Yes ☐ No ☐

Monsters: Real or Fake?

Activity 4 Monstrous Monsters

▶ **Complete the sentences.**
▶ **Read the text to your partner.**
▶ **Ask your partner to draw the monster.**
▶ **Compare your partner's sketch with the text.**

Flying reptile: Sketch 1

The monster _____*has*_____ a long body. It has _____*two*_____ _____*long*_____
        (verb)   (number)   (adjective)

wings. It has four _____*short*_____ tails. It has a _____*short*_____ neck.
                       (adjective)   (adjective)

It has _____*two*_____ _____*oval*_____ heads. On each head, it has _____*five*_____
       (number)   (adjective)   (number)

_____*small*_____ eyes and a _____*large*_____ mouth with sharp teeth. The monster
(adjective)   (adjective)

_____*is*_____ *blue, brown, etc.* .
(verb)   (colour)

Activity 4 Monstrous Monsters

▶ **Complete the sentences.**
▶ **Read the text to your partner.**
▶ **Ask your partner to draw the monster.**
▶ **Compare your partner's sketch with the text.**

Lake Monster: Sketch 1

The monster _____ *has* _____ a big body. It has _____ *two* _____ big humps.
        (verb)   (number)

It has two _____ *long* _____ tails and four _____ *short* _____ legs. It has three
        (adjective)   (adjective)

_____ *long* _____ necks. It has _____ *three* _____ *round* _____ heads. On each head,
 (adjective)   (number)   (adjective)

it has _____ *one* _____ *large* _____ eye and _____ *one* _____ *large* _____ mouth.
    (number)   (adjective)   (number)   (adjective)

The monster _____ *is* _____ *blue, brown, etc.* .
         (verb)   (colour)

- **I completed the description of a monster with ☐ or without ☐ help.**
- **I drew a monster according to my partner's description.**   Yes ☐   No ☐
- **I used Chatterbox 3 for help.**   Yes ☐   No ☐

Extension Activity

What a Monster!

► **Fill in the blanks.**
► **Use an adjective and a noun.**

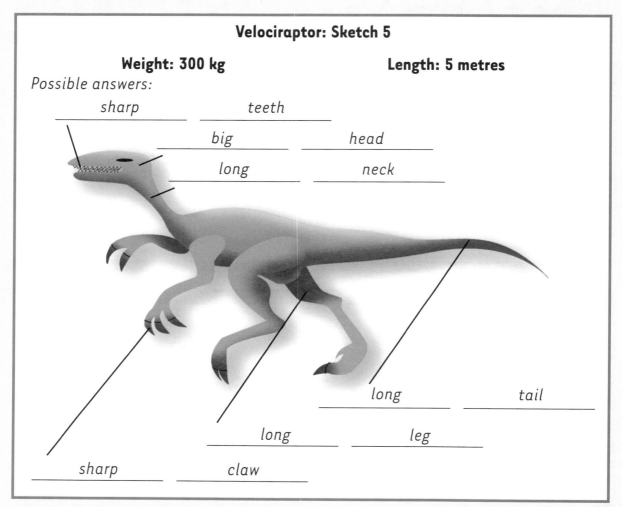

Velociraptor: Sketch 5

Weight: 300 kg   **Length: 5 metres**

Possible answers:

<u>sharp</u>   <u>teeth</u>

<u>big</u>   <u>head</u>

<u>long</u>   <u>neck</u>

<u>long</u>   <u>tail</u>

<u>long</u>   <u>leg</u>

<u>sharp</u>   <u>claw</u>   <u>long</u>

► **Write a short text that describes the monster.**

Possible answer: The velociraptor has sharp teeth. It has a big head and a long neck. It has two short legs and two long legs. It has sharp claws. It weighs 300 kg. It is five metres long.

Wrap-up

Your Movie Monster

▶ **Plan what your movie monster will look like.**
▶ **Complete each section about the monster.**

Answers will vary.

Animal

Measurements

(height)	(length)	(weight)

Special body parts

Special powers

Habitat

Name

Continued on next page

Monsters: Real or Fake?

▶ **Complete the fact card and write a text about your monster.**
▶ **Draw a sketch of your monster.**

Fact card

Name: *Answers will vary.* _____

Animal: _____

Measurements: _____

Special body parts: _____

Special powers: _____

Text	Sketch
_____	
_____	
_____	
_____	
_____	
_____	
_____	
_____	

- **I am satisfied with the movie monster I created with my partner.**
  Extremely ☐   Very ☐   Not very ☐   Not at all ☐

- **The text I wrote about the monster was:**
  Excellent ☐   Very good ☐   Fairly good ☐   Not very good ☐

- **My partner and I worked well together.**
  Always ☐   Most of the time ☐   Some of the time ☐   Never ☐

Dragons: Friends or Enemies?

There are hundreds of legends about dragons. In some legends, dragons are friendly creatures, but in other legends they are dangerous beasts.

▶ **Read the texts.**

In European legends, dragons are cruel and dangerous. They attack people. They look like huge lizards. They usually have scaly skin like a snake, strong legs, feet with claws, two wings and a long tail. Most Western dragons breathe fire and some are poisonous. Western dragons usually live in caves high up in the mountains where they hide their gold and jewels.

In Oriental legends, dragons are kind and intelligent. They guide people. Eastern dragons are composed of parts of different animals. They often have the body of a snake, the scales of a fish, the head of a camel, the claws of a tiger and the mane of a lion. They do not have wings. They do not breathe fire. Some Eastern dragons live on earth, while others live in the skies.

Continued on next page

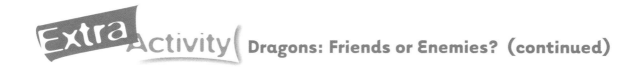

► **Compare the dragons.**
► **Describe their characters, physical characteristics and habitats.**

	Western Dragons	**Eastern Dragons**
Character	cruel and dangerous	kind and intelligent
Physical characteristics	look like lizards: scaly skin, strong legs, feet with claws, two wings, long tail, breathe fire, sometimes poisonous	have different body parts: body of a snake, scales of a fish, head of a camel, claws of a tiger, mane of a lion, do not have wings, do not breathe fire
Habitat	mountains caves	on earth in the skies

► **Write your own text about a dragon.**
► **Name your dragon.**
► **Describe its character, physical characteristics and habitat.**

Answers will vary.

_____

_____

_____

_____

Unit 7

Tall Tales

Warm-up

All about Tall Tales

▶ **Read the sentences about tall tales.**

▶ **Write the appropriate sentence in each speech bubble.**

The hero always has a problem.

Kids love to hear tall tales.

A tall tale always has exaggeration.

A tall tale always has a hero.

The hero always solves the problem in a clever or funny way.

* **I know some tall tales.** Yes ☐ No ☐

Tall Heroes

► **Name the heroes.**
► **Write one thing about each hero.**

John Henry

Johnny Appleseed

Paul Bunyan

Pecos Bill

He was a lumberjack. He could eat forty bowls of porridge for breakfast. He had a blue ox called Babe.

He was gentle but courageous. He wore a tin pot for a hat and never wore shoes. He walked across the land for forty-nine years. He planted apple trees.

He started working on the railroad when he was only three weeks old. He won a race against a machine.

He was a cowboy raised by coyotes. He was friends with wild animals. He rode a mountain lion. His whip was a live rattlesnake.

Activity 1 — Who's Who?

▶ **Match each character with the appropriate description.**
▶ **Write the character's name under the picture.**

Cucullin

Oonagh

Finn McCool

I am a clever person. I am happy. I like to help people.	I am a hard worker. I love my wife and family. I am gentle too.	I am the strongest giant in the country. I am the most powerful. I have defeated all the other giants.

▶ **With your partner, make a list of problems that people can have.**

• *Students will list four problems that people can have.*

_____

• _____

• _____

• _____

• **I can name the characters in the story.** Yes ☐ No ☐

• **My partner and I worked well together.**
  Always ☐ Most of the time ☐ Some of the time ☐ Never ☐

• **I used Chatterbox 3 for help.** Yes ☐ No ☐

Unit 7

Activity 2 Getting Ready

▶ **Answer the questions.**

Part 1: What I understand

1. What is Oonagh putting in the bread?

   frying pans

2. What is she collecting?

   large white stones

3. What does she tell Finn to do?

   to get into the baby's bed

Part 2: What I think

1. Why is Oonagh putting frying pans in the bread?

   to prove how strong Finn McCool is / to pretend that Finn can eat bread as hard

   as a rock

2. Why is she making curds?

   to pretend that Finn can squeeze water out of a stone

3. Why does she tell Finn McCool to get into the baby's bed?

   to pretend that Finn's baby is very strong

• **I gave my opinion.**	Yes ☐	No ☐
• **I found a funny solution to the problem.**	Yes ☐	No ☐

Activity 3 A Surprise for Cucullin

▶ **Answer the questions.**

1. What does Oonagh ask Cucullin to do? Why?

   to turn the house around because it was very windy

2. Where is Cucullin's strength?

   in the middle finger of his right hand

3. What did Oonagh give Cucullin to eat?

   a loaf of bread

4. What happened to Cucullin?

   He bit into the bread and broke four of his teeth.

5. Why was Cucullin amazed?

   Finn's baby was able to eat the bread with no problem.

▶ **Find an example of exaggeration in this part of the story.**

turning the house around; having power in one finger; eating bread with a frying

pan in it

▶ **Predict how the story will end.**

Students will say how they think the story

will end.

	Yes ☐	No ☐
• **I predicted the ending of the story.**	Yes ☐	No ☐
• **I used Chatterbox 6 for help.**	Yes ☐	No ☐

Activity 4 A Real Hero

▶ **Find out why "The Story of Finn McCool" is a tall tale.**
▶ **Read the sentences.**
▶ **Place each sentence in the appropriate box.**

1. Finn McCool, Cucullin and Oonagh are giants.

2. Cucullin wants to fight Finn, but Finn doesn't want to.

3. Cucullin is so strong that he can destroy thunderbolts.

4. Finn can eat bread as hard as a rock, and he can squeeze water from a stone.

5. All of Cucullin's power is in the middle finger of his right hand.

6. Finn bites Cucullin's finger and takes his power away.

7. Oonagh is a clever woman who tricks the giant Cucullin.

8. The giant Cucullin runs away.

Problem
2. Cucullin wants to fight Finn, but Finn doesn't want to.

Hero
7. Oonagh is a clever woman who tricks the giant Cucullin.

Continued on next page

Exaggeration
1. Finn McCool, Cucullin and Oonagh are giants.
3. Cucullin is so strong that he can destroy thunderbolts.
4. Finn can eat bread as hard as a rock, and he can squeeze water from a stone.
5. All of Cucullin's power is in the middle finger of his right hand.

Solution
6. Finn bites Cucullin's finger and takes his power away.
8. The giant Cucullin runs away.

- **I think** _____ **is the hero because** _____ .

- **My favourite character is** _____ **because**
_____ .

- **I liked this story.**   Yes ☐   No ☐

Wrap-up

▶ **Create your own tall tale.** *Students will write their own tall tales.*

_____

_____

_____

_____

_____

_____

_____

_____ was the _____ person in
     (hero's name)   (adjective)

the whole _____ . _____ was so
                        (place)   (he or she)

_____ that the other people in _____
          (adjective)   (place)

always went to _____ when they had a problem.
                    (him or her)

Let me tell you how it all started. One day _____ went
                                                      (character's name)

to see _____ . "Please help me," said _____ .
           (hero's name)   (character's name)

"I have a big problem and I don't know what to do."

Continued on next page

"What is the problem?" asked _____ . "Well," said
(hero's name)

_____ , "here's what happened: _____
(character's name)   (Describe the problem.)

_____

_____ ."

"Don't worry," said _____ . "I know what to do." So, here's
(hero's name)

what _____ did: _____
(hero's name)   (Write the solution to the problem.)

_____ .

That's why everybody in _____ now goes to _____
(place)   (hero's name)

whenever they need help.

- **I told a tall tale about** _____ .
- **My partners liked my tall tale.**   Yes ☐   No ☐
- **During this unit, I worked:**
  Very hard ☐   Moderately hard ☐   Not very hard ☐   Not hard at all ☐

The Flying Horse

► **Read about Alexis-le-trotteur.**

Alexis Lapointe was born in 1860 on a farm in Saint-Étienne-de-Malbaie.
When he was a young boy, he loved horses and races. He thought he was a horse
himself because he could run so fast. People said he could run faster than anyone or
anything. He could even run faster than a train. He could perform many superhuman
feats. Alexis' nickname was "The Flying Horse of the Saguenay."

Continued on next page

▶ **Fill in the blanks to invent your own story about Alexis-le-trotteur.**

Students will finish each sentence in order to create their own tales about Alexis-le-trotteur.

One day, Alexis was walking in the village when someone told him that _____

_____

_____ .

Then Alexis thought about what he could do. He decided to _____

_____

_____ .

While Alexis was doing that, the people of the village were _____

_____ .

_____

Everybody was so happy that Alexis was able to _____

_____

_____ .

From then on, whenever someone had a problem, who did they call?

That's right! Alexis, The Flying Horse of the Saguenay.

©ERPI Please do not photocopy this page.

Unit 8

The Case of the Stolen Guitar

Warm-up

Popular Detectives

▶ **Identify the detectives and their qualities.**

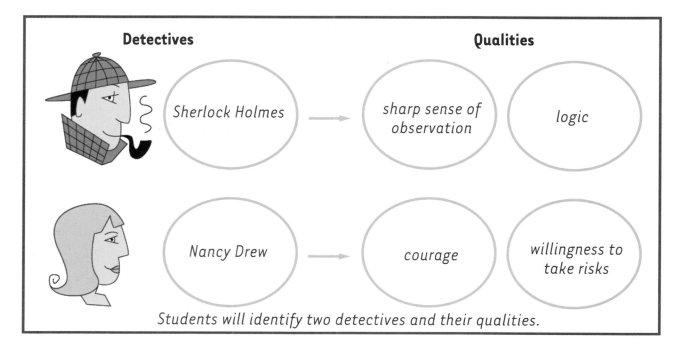

Students will identify two detectives and their qualities.

▶ **Name your favourite detective.**
▶ **Find some classmates who like the same detective as you.**
▶ **Ask for their signatures.**   Students will name their favourite detectives.

Signature

Favourite Detective

• **I can talk about my favourite detective.**   Yes ☐   No ☐

Activity 1 The Art of Being a Detective

▶ Get ready to listen to a detective.
▶ Match each word in the Word Box with its illustration.

   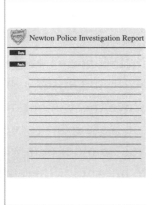

_____ suspect _____   _____ fingerprints _____   _____ witness _____   _____ police report _____

  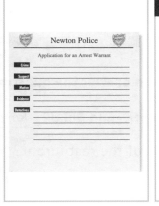

Word Box

alibi
arrest warrant
fingerprints
footprint
police report
suspect
witness

_____ alibi _____   _____ footprint _____   _____ arrest warrant _____

▶ Listen to a detective.
▶ Write the numbers in the appropriate order.

_8_   _2_   _5_   _6_   _1_   _3_   _4_   _7_

• **I identified the main steps in an investigation.**   Yes ☐   No ☐

The Case of the Stolen Guitar

How Embarrassing!

▶ **Read the text.**
▶ **Pay attention to the details.**

A Most Embarrassing Moment
by Lynn Robertson

Last Monday I went to The Steak Palace with my boyfriend Rosario. We left at 6:00 p.m. We drove there in our new convertible. We arrived at the restaurant fifteen minutes later. The waiter was an older man with grey hair. He showed us to our table. There was a vase with yellow roses on the table. What a romantic place!

I ordered a steak and a salad. My boyfriend took chicken. At 8:30 p.m. we started eating our dessert, apple pie with ice cream. Suddenly we heard loud noises coming from the kitchen. "Get out of here! Get out of here!" someone shouted in an angry voice. We saw a big white cat running out of the kitchen. It had a fish in its mouth. The cat looked everywhere. When it saw me, it jumped into my arms. It was Leo my cat! I was so embarrassed.

▶ **Cover the text and then answer the questions.**

1. What is Lynn's boyfriend called? _Rosario_

2. What is the name of the restaurant? _The Steak Palace_

3. What time did Lynn and her boyfriend arrive at the restaurant? _6:15 p.m._

4. What day was it? _Monday_

5. What colour was the waiter's hair? _grey_

6. What colour were the roses? _yellow_

7. What did Rosario order for supper? _chicken_

8. What did Lynn eat for dessert? _apple pie with ice cream_

9. What did the cat have in its mouth? _a fish_

10. What is the cat's name? _Leo_

Activity 2 The Stolen Guitar

Newtown Police
Detective Notebook

Detectives

1. _Students will write their own names._   **3.** _____

2. _____   **4.** _____

Facts

What happened? _Jimmy Dee's bass guitar disappeared._

What does the stolen guitar look like? _____

four-string guitar; colour: red; brand name: Jupiter; serial number XZT-3658

_____

Who are the members of Jimmy's band? _Jimmy Dee (bass guitarist), Kioko_

(singer), Nicky (guitarist), Ayiana (drummer), Brandon (singer)

_____

Where did the crime take place? _Newtown Art Centre_

When did the crime take place? _Between Friday evening, (July 15) 6:30 p.m._

and Saturday morning (July 16) 9:30 a.m.

What clues did the police find at the scene of the crime? _Dressing room: no_

break-in / Fingerprints: on the door knob of the dressing room / Footprints:

outside, below the large window next to the entrance. Running shoes, size 9

- **I identified the important information.**   Yes ☐   No ☐
- **I used Chatterbox 8 for help.**   Yes ☐   No ☐

Activity 3 What Do You Know?

Name: _Jimmy Dee_

Occupation: _Bass guitarist of "The Shiny Stars"_

Jimmy Dee left his guitar: on the stage ☐ **in his dressing room** ☑ **in his car** ☐.

He left for supper at: 6:00 p.m. ☐ **6:30 p.m.** ☑ **7:00 p.m.** ☐.

He left the door of his dressing room: open ☐ **closed** ☐ **locked** ☑.

He was: alone ☐ **with someone** ☑. **Specify:** _Kioko_

He was at Aristo's Restaurant from 6:45 p.m. to _10:00 p.m._ .

He got back to his hotel room at _10:30 p.m._ .

He was: alone ☐ **with someone** ☑. **Specify:** _Nicky_

Name: _Bob Wilson_

Occupation: _Janitor for Newtown Art Centre_

He arrived at work at: 7:00 p.m. ☐ **7:30 p.m.** ☐ **8:00 p.m.** ☑.

The door of Newtown Art Centre was: open ☐ **locked** ☑ **unlocked** ☐.

There was an extra set of keys:
in the janitor's car ☐ **at the director's house** ☐ **in the office** ☑.

The window next to the entrance was: closed ☑ **open** ☐ **broken** ☐.

Bob Wilson closed ☐ **opened** ☑ **broke** ☐ **the window.**

At 9:30 p.m., he heard: a scream ☐ **footsteps** ☑ **a dog barking** ☐.

He went to Jimmy Dee's dressing room at _10:30 p.m._ .

The door of the dressing room was: open ☐ **unlocked** ☐ **locked** ☑.

The bass guitar was in the dressing room. Yes ☐ **No** ☑ .

Bob Wilson finished work at _11:00 p.m._ .

- **I discovered more clues when I listened to the interviews.** Yes ☐ No ☐

Activity **4** Who Did It?

Suspect: Jimmy Dee		**Occupation:** Bass guitarist (The Shiny Stars)
Time	**Alibi**	**Fingerprint**
6:30	Went to restaurant with Kioko.	Students will
6:45	Arrived at restaurant.	glue fingerprint
10:00	Left restaurant, back to hotel, talked with Nicky.	#3 here.
10:45	Went to bed.	

Clues: Valid alibi.

Fingerprints (#3) on door knob of dressing room

Shoe size: 9

Suspect: Kioko		**Occupation:** Singer (The Shiny Stars)
Time	**Alibi**	**Fingerprint**
6:30	Went to restaurant with Jimmy.	Students will
6:45	Arrived at restaurant.	glue fingerprint
9:00	Returned to hotel by taxi; went to bed.	#2 here.
10:30	Woken up by Ayiana, her roommate.	

Clues: No valid alibi between 9:00 p.m. and 10:30 p.m.

Fingerprints (#2) on door knob of dressing room

Shoe size: 7

©ERPI Please do not photocopy this page.

Continued on next page

The Case of the Stolen Guitar

Activity 4 Who Did It? (continued)

Suspect: Nicky		Occupation: Guitarist (The Shiny Stars)
Time	**Alibi**	**Fingerprint**
6:30	Went to restaurant with partners.	Students will glue fingerprint #1 here.
6:45	Arrived at restaurant.	
10:00	Left restaurant, back to hotel, talked with Jimmy.	
10:45	Went to bed.	
Clues: Valid alibi.		
Fingerprints (#1) on door knob of dressing room		
Shoe size: 11		

Suspect: Gerry		Occupation: Singer in another rock group
Time	**Alibi**	**Fingerprint**
6:30	Arrived at restaurant with boyfriend.	Students will glue fingerprint #6 here.
9:00	Left restaurant; drove boyfriend home.	
9:45	Got home, listened to music.	
11:30	Went to bed.	
Clues: No valid alibi after 9:45 p.m. She lives alone.		
Shoe size: 9		

Continued on next page

Activity 4 Who Did It? (continued)

Suspect: Bob Wilson		Occupation: Janitor, Newtown Art Centre	
Time	**Alibi**		**Fingerprint**
8:00	Arrived at Newtown Art Centre by car.		Students will
9:30	Heard a noise during coffee break.		glue fingerprint
11:00	Left for home.		#5 here.
11:15	Arrived home; went to bed ten minutes later.		
Clues: No valid alibi.			
Fingerprints (#5) on door knob of dressing room			
Shoe size: 10			

Suspect: Raffaëlla		Occupation: Collector of rock-star objects	
Time	**Alibi**		**Fingerprint**
6:00	Went to restaurant with Vladimir.		Students will
9:00	Left restaurant.		glue fingerprint
9:30	Arrived home, watched TV.		#4 here.
11:00	Went to bed.		
Clues: No valid alibi after 9:00 p.m. She lives alone.			
Fingerprints (#4) on door knob of dressing room			
Shoe size: 9			

Continued on next page

The Case of the Stolen Guitar

Activity 4 Who Did It? (continued)

Suspect: *Vladimir*		Occupation: *Seller of high-priced guitars*
Time	**Alibi**	**Fingerprint**
6:00	*Went to restaurant with Raffaëlla.*	*Students will*
9:00	*Left restaurant and went to movies.*	*glue fingerprint*
12:00	*Arrived home and went to bed.*	*#7 here.*
Clues: *No valid alibi after 9:00 p.m. He lives alone.*		
Shoe size: 10		

Suspect: *Moira*		Occupation: *Mayor of Newtown*
Time	**Alibi**	**Fingerprint**
6:00	*Arrived at benefit dinner.*	*Students will*
10:15	*Left benefit dinner, went home, took a bath.*	*glue fingerprint*
11:30	*Went to bed.*	*#8 here.*
Clues: *Valid alibi until 10:15 p.m.*		
Shoe size: 8		

- **I identified the suspects and their occupations.**
  All of them ☐   Most of them ☐   Some of them ☐   None of them ☐
- **I used Chatterbox 9 for help.**   Yes ☐   No ☐

Wrap-up

▶ **Fill in the form to apply for an arrest warrant.**

 Newtown Police

Application for an Arrest Warrant

Crime   *Theft of a bass guitar*

Suspect   *Raffaëlla*

Motive   <u>She wanted to add Jimmy Dee's guitar to her collection of</u> <u>rock-star objects.</u>

Evidence   *Her fingerprints are on the door knob for no valid reason; she has no* *valid alibi; she wears size 9 shoes.*

Detectives   *Students will write their own names.*

Additional information: Raffaëlla ate at the same restaurant as Jimmy *and his group. She left the restaurant at 9:00 p.m. and went to the* *Newtown Art Centre. She entered the front office by climbing through* *the open window. She took the key to Jimmy's dressing room, unlocked* *it and stole the guitar. She relocked the door, returned the key and left* *through the front door.*

- **I spoke English with my partners.**
  Always ☐   Most of the time ☐   Some of the time ☐   Never ☐
- **I did my share of the work.**
  Always ☐   Most of the time ☐   Some of the time ☐   Never ☐
- **I liked this activity.**   Yes ☐   No ☐

► **Read the text.**

Five bicycles were stolen: a white one, a yellow one, a green one, a silver one and a blue one. The bicycles belonged to five students from your school: Jacob, Sue-Ming, Ari, Jessica and Melanie. The thief sent a letter to the Chief Inspector.

Dear Chief Inspector:

If you can solve this puzzle, I will return the bicycles: Which colour is each student's bicycle?

Melanie doesn't like white or silver.
Jessica doesn't like blue or yellow.
Jacob likes white and silver.
Sue-Ming doesn't have a yellow bike.
The green and silver bicycles belong to boys.
The yellow bicycle belongs to a girl.

Sincerely,

The bicycle thief

► **Solve the puzzle.**
► **Find out who owns each bicycle.**

	Bicycles				
	White	**Yellow**	**Green**	**Silver**	**Blue**
Jacob				✓	
Sue-Ming					✓
Ari			✓		
Jessica	✓				
Melanie		✓			

Unit 9

Loonies and Toonies!

Warm-up

The Characteristics of Money

▶ **Evaluate your coin.**

▶ **Answer the questions below.**

Coin: *Students will evaluate one coin.*

Is it easy to carry?	Yes ☐	No ☐
Does everyone accept it as money?	Yes ☐	No ☐
Is it easy to identify the value of the coin?	Yes ☐	No ☐
Is it solid and durable?	Yes ☐	No ☐
Is it difficult to copy?	Yes ☐	No ☐

▶ **Guess which of these objects could be used as money.**

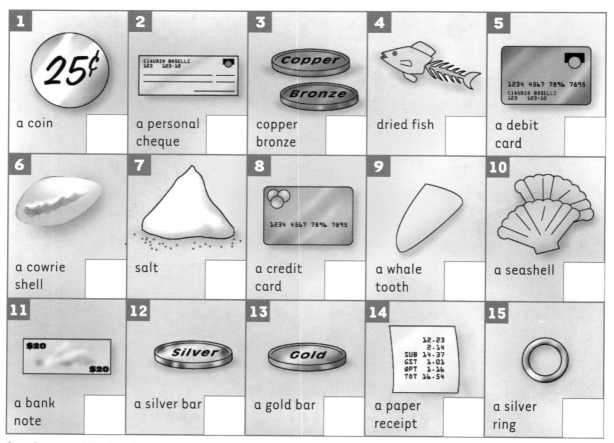

1 a coin	2 a personal cheque	3 copper bronze	4 dried fish	5 a debit card
6 a cowrie shell	7 salt	8 a credit card	9 a whale tooth	10 a seashell
11 a bank note	12 a silver bar	13 a gold bar	14 a paper receipt	15 a silver ring

Students will check off the objects they think can be used as money.

- **I gave my opinion about objects that could be used as money.** Yes ☐ No ☐
- **I used Chatterbox 6 for help.** Yes ☐ No ☐

Unit 9

Activity 1

Money Makes the World Go Round

▶ **Identify each object on the timeline.**

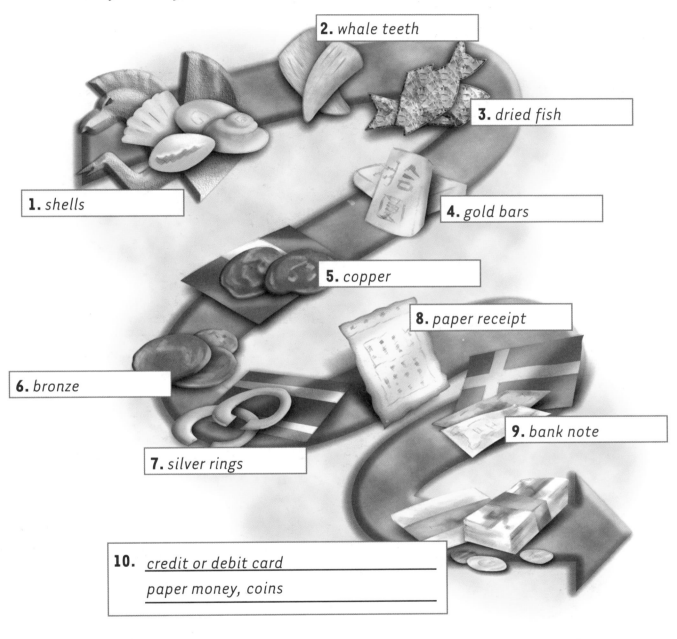

2. *whale teeth*

3. *dried fish*

1. *shells*

4. *gold bars*

5. *copper*

8. *paper receipt*

6. *bronze*

9. *bank note*

7. *silver rings*

10. credit or debit card

paper money, coins

- **My predictions were correct.**
  All of them ☐   Most of them ☐   Some of them ☐   None of them ☐
- **I can name the objects that were used as money.**
  All of them ☐   Most of them ☐   Some of them ☐   None of them ☐

Looking Ahead

► Think about how money has changed over time.
► Design the money of the future.

Students will design the money of the future.

Activity 2 Coins and Culture

► **Complete the coin cards.**

Students will complete the coin cards with information from handout 44.

Name: *penny*

Value: *one cent*

Symbol: *two maple leaves*

Name: *nickel*

Value: *five cents*

Symbol: *beaver*

Name: *dime*

Value: *ten cents*

Symbol: *schooner*

Name: *quarter*

Value: *twenty-five cents*

Symbol: *caribou*

Name: *loonie*

Value: *one dollar*

Symbol: *loon*

Name: *toonie*

Value: *two dollars*

Symbol: *polar bear*

- **I told my partners about the** _____ **coin. It is called a** _____ .
- **I used Chatterbox 14 for help.**   Yes ☐   No ☐

Activity 3 Let's Remember

▶ **Guess what each of the coins honours.**

1
2
3
4
5
6
7
8
9
10

A. The Raven Bringing Light to the World

B. The Canadian Ballet's 50th Anniversary of First Performance

C. The Montréal Olympic Games

D. The International Year of Older Persons

E. The International Year of the Child

F. Sugaring Off

G. The International Year of Peace

H. The 75th Anniversary of Canada's First Nobel Prize for the Discovery of Insulin

I. The McIntosh Apple

J. One Hundred Years of the RCMP

Answers: 1-D; 2-I; 3-E; 4-B; 5-J; 6-H; 7-G; 8-C; 9-A; 10-F

- **I understood the interview.**
  All of it ☐   Most of it ☐   Some of it ☐   None of it ☐

- **I liked learning about commemorative coins because** _____

  _____ .

► **Choose five symbols that represent where you live.**

Students will indicate five symbols that represent their communities.

_____   _____

- **The things that represent my community are** _____
  because _____ .
- **I honoured** _____ **on my coin.**
- **I used Chatterbox 12 for help.**   Yes ☐   No ☐

SB 89

Wrap-up

► **Design your own class money.**
► **Describe your coin.**

Name: *Students will design and describe a class coin.* _____

Value: _____

Description: _____

_____

- **I am satisfied with my work.**
  Extremely ☐   Very ☐   Not very ☐   Not at all ☐
- **During this unit, I worked:**
  Very hard ☐   Moderately hard ☐   Not very hard ☐   Not hard at all ☐

Money Math

► **Solve the math problems below.**

1. Anushri bought a bag of treats for $0.99. She paid with nine coins. Which coins did she use?

    She used three quarters ($0.75), two dimes ($0.20), four pennies ($0.04).

    ◯ ◯ ◯ ◯ ◯ ◯ ◯ ◯ ◯

2. Jordan has $5.00 in his piggy bank. He has sixteen coins, which include toonies, loonies, quarters and dimes. How many of each coin does he have?

    He has one toonie ($2), one loonie ($1), four quarters ($1) and ten dimes ($1).

    ◯ ◯ ◯ ◯ ◯ ◯ ◯ ◯
    ◯ ◯ ◯ ◯ ◯ ◯ ◯ ◯

3. Francisco loves candy. He bought three gummies, three bubble gums, two candy rolls and one lollipop. Gummies are a nickel each. Bubble gums are three for a quarter. Candy rolls are a quarter each. Lollipops are a dime each. How much did he spend?

    He spent $1.

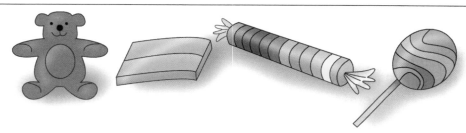

Unit 10

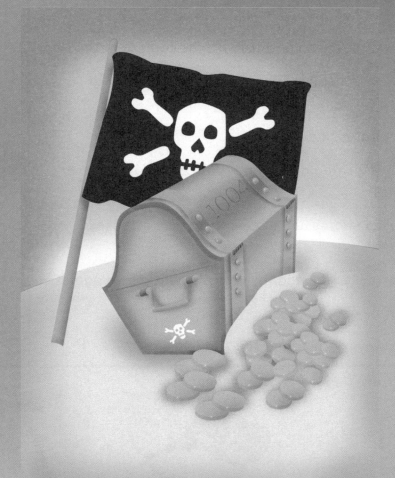

Treasure Hunters

Warm-up

What Do You Think?

▶ **Read the statements.**

▶ **Put a check mark (✓) in the appropriate column.**

		True	False
1.	Only men were pirates.		✓
2.	Most pirates had a wooden leg.		✓
3.	Pirates had to sign a contract with the captain of the ship.	✓	
4.	Pirates were generous. They shared their booty with poor people.		✓
5.	The best pirates had big ships.		✓
6.	All pirate ships flew a black flag with a skull and crossbones.		✓
7.	Pirates used swords and pistols when they attacked other ships.	✓	
8.	Pirates attacked merchant ships to steal their valuables.	✓	
9.	Pirates stole only money and jewels.		✓
10.	Pirates always buried their treasure.		✓

For extra details, see the Answer Key, handout 47.

- **I participated in the discussion with my partners.**
  Always ☐   Most of the time ☐   Some of the time ☐   Never ☐
- **I encouraged my partners.**
  Always ☐   Most of the time ☐   Some of the time ☐   Never ☐
- **I used Chatterbox 7 for help.**   Yes ☐   No ☐

Dirty Jane and the Pirates

▶ **Complete the story map.**

Title: Dirty Jane and the Pirates

Characters: Dirty Jane, Big Henry,

John Longhands, other pirates

Setting: pirate ship, Caribbean Sea

Storyline

▶ **Place the events in the appropriate order.**

A. Thirty days later Dirty Jane sailed away from the island on another ship.

B. Dirty Jane was the captain of a pirate ship.

C. Dirty Jane buried the treasure on the island and drew a map.

D. One day Dirty Jane demanded a larger share of the booty.

E. That night the ship hit something during a violent storm.

F. The next morning Dirty Jane took the last lifeboat and rowed to an island.

G. The pirates got angry and made Dirty Jane their prisoner.

H. The pirates quickly abandoned ship.

1. _B_ ➡ 2. _D_ ➡ 3. _G_ ➡ 4. _E_ ➡ 5. _H_ ➡ 6. _F_ ➡ 7. _C_ ➡ 8. _A_

Theme

The story is about: panic ◯ anger ◯ greed ✓.

Dirty Jane lost her crew and probably her treasure because _____
she was greedy   .

- **I understood how to complete the story map.**   Yes ☐   No ☐
- **I completed the story map with ☐ or without ☐ help.**

Activity 2 Buried Treasure

▶ Trace the route.
▶ Find the buried treasure.

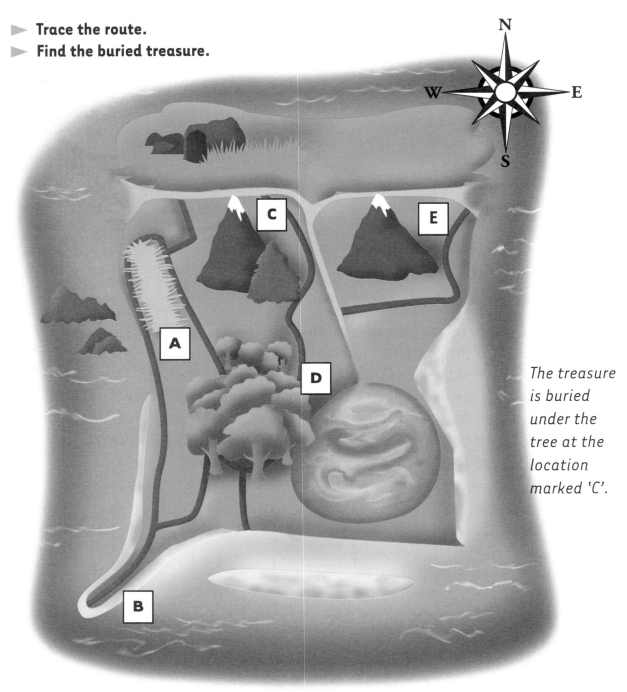

The treasure is buried under the tree at the location marked 'C'.

- **I understood the key words.**
  All of them ☐   Most of them ☐   Some of them ☐   None of them ☐
- **I found the buried treasure.**   Yes ☐   No ☐

Activity 3 Find My Treasure

My treasure

	A	B	C	D	E	F	G	H	I
1					Start				
2									
3									
4									
5	Start								Start
6									
7									
8									
9					Start				

My partner's treasure

	A	B	C	D	E	F	G	H	I
1					Start				
2									
3									
4									
5	Start								Start
6									
7									
8									
9					Start				

My crew

- I understood the rules of the game. Yes ☐ No ☐
- I used direction words to move my crew. Yes ☐ No ☐

Treasure Hunters

Activity 4 Get Your Gear!

▶ **Write one use for each object.**

Answers are examples only.

To protect my feet

_____

_____

To find my way around

in case I get lost

_____

To take care of an

injury

_____

To see at night or in a

dark cave

_____

To eat when I am

hungry

_____

To drink when I am

thirsty

_____

To protect my head

from falling rocks

_____

To wear on a boat or to

swim across a lake

_____

Continued on next page

Activity 4   **Get Your Gear! (continued)**

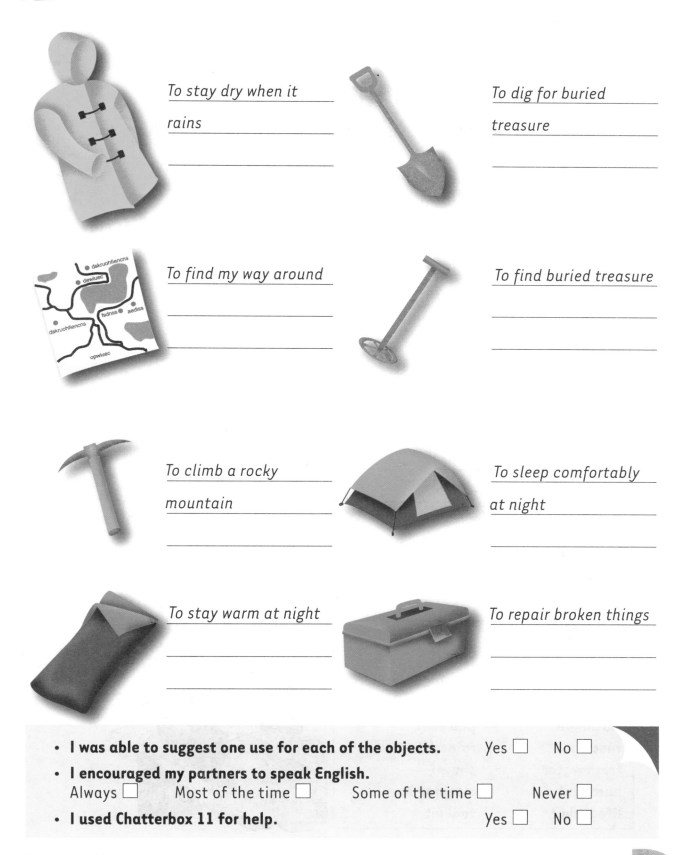

To stay dry when it
rains

To dig for buried
treasure

To find my way around

To find buried treasure

To climb a rocky
mountain

To sleep comfortably
at night

To stay warm at night

To repair broken things

- **I was able to suggest one use for each of the objects.**   Yes ☐   No ☐
- **I encouraged my partners to speak English.**
  Always ☐   Most of the time ☐   Some of the time ☐   Never ☐
- **I used Chatterbox 11 for help.**   Yes ☐   No ☐

Get Your Gear!

► Identify the right piece of equipment for each situation.

1. I need _____*a hard-hat*_____ to protect my head from falling rocks.

2. I need _____*a shovel*_____ to dig for buried treasure.

3. I need _____*fresh water*_____ to drink when I get thirsty.

4. I need _____*a raincoat*_____ and _____*boots*_____ to stay dry when it rains.

5. I need _____*a life jacket*_____ to swim across a lake.

6. I need _____*a tool kit*_____ to repair my ship.

7. I need _____*a map*_____ and _____*a compass*_____ to find my way around.

8. I need _____*a flashlight*_____ to see in the dark.

9. I need _____*a metal detector*_____ to locate buried treasure.

10. I need _____*food*_____ to eat when I get hungry.

11. I need _____*a pup tent*_____ and _____*a sleeping bag*_____ to sleep comfortably outdoors.

12. I need _____*a pickaxe*_____ to climb a rocky mountain.

13. I need _____*a first-aid kit*_____ to look after myself in case I get hurt.

Word Box

boots	map
compass	metal detector
first-aid kit	pickaxe
flashlight	pup tent
food	raincoat
fresh water	shovel
hard-hat	sleeping bag
life jacket	tool kit

I need a flashlight to see in the dark.

Wrap-up

▶ **Write down ten items to take on the treasure hunt.**

Essential Gear

1. *Students will write down ten items to take on a treasure hunt.*
2. _____
3. _____
4. _____
5. _____
6. _____
7. _____
8. _____
9. _____
10. _____

▶ **Write one question about the story.**
▶ **Write the answer to your question.**

Question: *Students will write a question and the correct answer.*

_____

Answer: _____

_____

- **I prepared my list of ten items.**   Yes ☐   No ☐
- **I wrote a question about the story.**   Yes ☐   No ☐
- **I spoke English.**
  Always ☐   Most of the time ☐   Some of the time ☐   Never ☐

 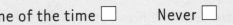

The Jolly Roger

Pirates used flags to scare people. The flag was called *Jolly Roger*. The most common flag was black with a skull and crossbones. Pirates flew many other flags. Each flag was designed to show how cruel the pirates were.

► **Read the following texts.**
► **Write the name of the pirate under each flag.**

Calico Jack

Jack Rackham was a pirate called Calico Jack. Like many pirates, he had a skull on his flag. His flag also had two crossed swords, which showed that he was very willing to fight.

Thomas Tew

Thomas Tew's flag showed that he would not hesitate to fight. His flag was black and had a fist holding a sword.

Black Beard

Edward Teach (Blackbeard) was very cruel. His flag was equally cruel. It showed a skeleton holding a spear pointing to a bleeding heart.

Edward Teach (Blackbeard)

Jack Rackham (Calico Jack)

Thomas Tew

Unit 11

Don't Bug Me!

Survey Sheet

► **Ask your partners the questions.**
► **If the answer is yes, put a check mark (✓).**
► **If the answer is no, put an X.**

Students will survey their partners and note their answers on the survey sheet.

Question	Name: _____	Name: _____	Name: _____
1. Do bees bug you?			
2. Do mosquitoes bug you?			
3. Do crickets bug you?			
4. Do ants bug you?			

Continued on next page

102 one hundred and two

Unit 11

Question	Name: _____	Name: _____	Name: _____
5. Do flies bug you?			
6. Do fleas bug you?			
7. Do cockroaches bug you?			
8. Do centipedes bug you?			

- I interviewed my partners and found out that _____ doesn't like _____ .
- I don't like _____ because _____ _____ .

Activity 1 Don't Let the Bugs Bite!

► Classify the insects as harmful or not harmful.
► Write the name of each insect in the appropriate place.

bee   ant   cockroach   centipede   flea   fly   mosquito   cricket

Not harmful

_____
_____
_____
_____
_____
_____

Harmful

_____
_____
_____
_____
_____
_____

Students will write the names of the insects that they believe are harmful or not harmful.

- **I classified the insects.**
  All of them ☐   Most of them ☐   Some of them ☐   None of them ☐
- **I used Chatterbox 15 for help.**   Yes ☐   No ☐

SB
106·108

► **Fill in the information about each insect.**

Name: *mosquito*

Habitat: *cool, dark places; water*

Two characteristics: *females bite;*
eat at night; spread diseases

Harmful or not harmful: *harmful*

Name: *ant*

Habitat: *colonies*

Two characteristics: *tiny, very strong;*
eat small insects, nectar and
honeydew; social; live like a family;
communicate with each other

Harmful or not harmful: *not harmful*

Name: *fly*

Habitat: *garbage and rotten food*

Two characteristics: *common; seen*
in spring and summer; move quickly;
sense movement; carry bacteria

Harmful or not harmful: *harmful*

Name: *bee*

Habitat: *colony; nest*

Two characteristics: *females sting;*
good for environment; help fruit and veg-
etables grow; collect nectar and pollen;
one queen and many workers; sometimes
80 000 workers; look after their babies

Harmful or not harmful: *harmful*

©**ERPI** Please do not photocopy this page.

Continued on next page

Don't Bug Me!

Activity 2   The Bug File (continued)

Name: *flea*

Habitat: *hair and clothing*

Two characteristics: *tiny; bite; jump from person to person*

Harmful or not harmful: *harmful*

Name: *cricket*

Habitat: *fields and backyards*

Two characteristics: *males sing to attract females; heard from spring to fall; small; eat young plants*

Harmful or not harmful: *not harmful*

Name: *cockroach*

Habitat: *dark, damp places; old buildings and houses; dirty places*

Two characteristics: *slip through cracks in walls; hide during the day; eat at night; eat anything*

Harmful or not harmful: *not harmful*

Name: *centipede*

Habitat: *dead leaves; trees; basements*

Two characteristics: *don't all have 100 legs; between 30 and 340 legs; front legs are poisonous fangs; catch other insects with them; bite humans*

Harmful or not harmful: *harmful*

- **My predictions were correct.**
  All of them ☐   Most of them ☐   Some of them ☐   None of them ☐
- **I told my partners about** _____ **and** _____ .
- **I paid attention to my partners when they were talking.**
  Always ☐   Most of the time ☐   Some of the time ☐   Never ☐
- **I used Chatterbox 9 for help.**   Yes ☐   No ☐

Activity 3 Get a Job!

▶ Write down the eight occupations.
▶ Find a job for each insect.

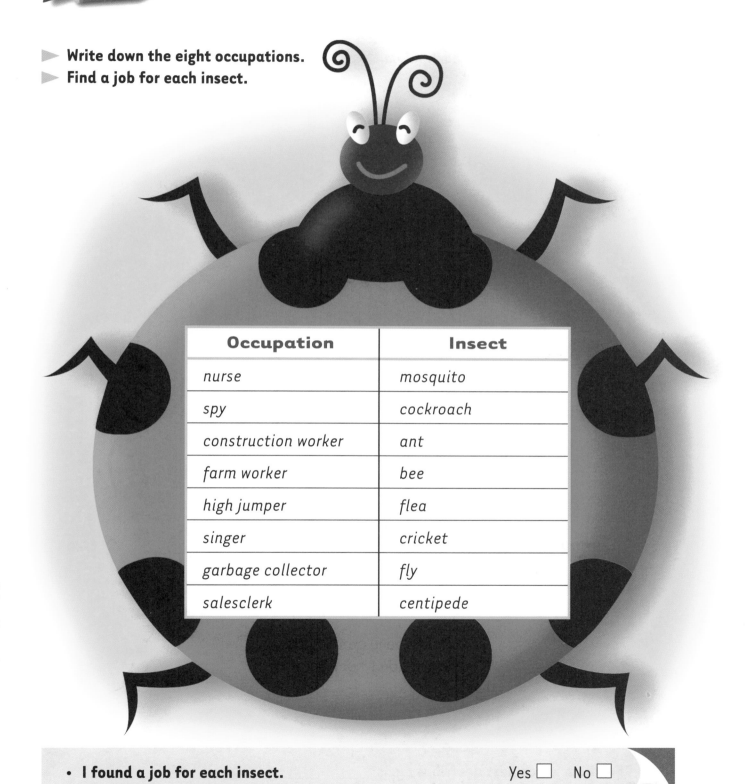

Occupation	Insect
nurse	mosquito
spy	cockroach
construction worker	ant
farm worker	bee
high jumper	flea
singer	cricket
garbage collector	fly
salesclerk	centipede

- I found a job for each insect.   Yes ☐   No ☐
- I liked this activity.   Yes ☐   No ☐

Activity 4 — What Did You Call Me?

▶ **Find the insect to complete each idiom.**

He works all the time.
He is as busy as a __bee__ .

She is always moving.
She has __ants__ in her pants.

He's a very gentle person.
He wouldn't hurt a __fly__ .

- **The idiom which best describes me is** _____

_____ .

Unit 11

Snug as a Bug

▶ **Illustrate the four idioms you learned in activity 4.**

<table>
<tr>
<td>

Students will illustrate the four idioms.

</td>
<td></td>
</tr>
<tr>
<td></td>
<td></td>
</tr>
</table>

▶ **Think about the characteristics of the insects you learned about in this unit.**

▶ **Invent an idiom for one of the insects.**

Answers will vary.

_____

► **Complete the ID card for one insect.**

Insect Description

Name: _____

Habitat: _____

_____

Characteristics: _____

Students will choose an insect and provide information about its

habitat and its characteristics.

_____

_____

_____

- **I made an ID card for** _____ .
- **During this unit, I worked:**
  Very hard ☐   Moderately hard ☐   Not very hard ☐   Not hard at all ☐

Bug Fun

► Find the name for each treat.

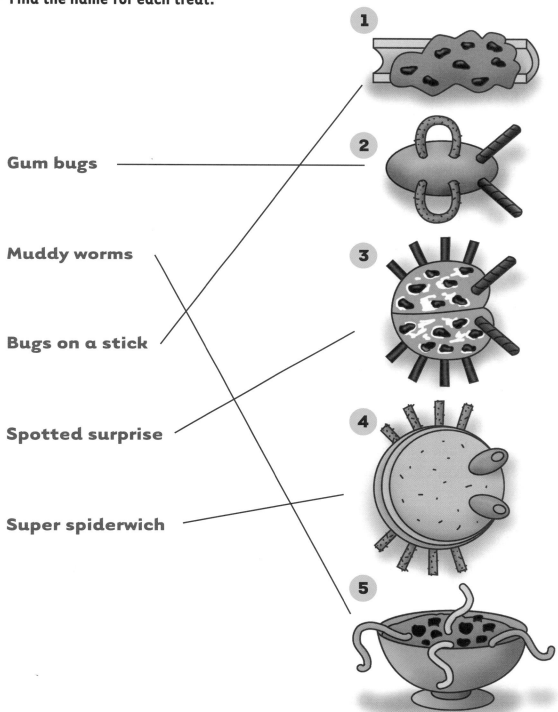

Gum bugs

Muddy worms

Bugs on a stick

Spotted surprise

Super spiderwich

Continued on next page

Don't Bug Me!

▶ **Find out how to make your own insect treats.**

Bugs on a stick

Ingredients: Celery sticks, peanut butter or cream cheese, raisins
Directions: Spread peanut butter on the celery sticks. Push the raisins into the peanut butter.

Gum bugs

Ingredients: Large gumdrops, round pretzels broken in half, two pieces of black licorice string
Directions: Make two little holes in the top of the gumdrop. Push the pieces of black licorice into the holes to make antennae. Take the two pieces of pretzel and push them into the side of the gumdrop for wings.

Spotted surprise

Ingredients: A red apple, peanut butter or cream cheese, raisins, black licorice string
Directions: Cut the apple in half and put the white side down. Slice the apple in half again to make the ladybug's wings. Put some peanut butter or cream cheese on the raisins and stick them on the apple to make the ladybug's spots. Cut the black licorice string into small pieces for legs and antennae.

Super spiderwich

Ingredients: Two slices of round bread, any sandwich filling, pretzels, olives
Directions: Make a sandwich. Put four pretzels on each side for the legs. Place two olives on the top for the eyes.

Muddy worms

Ingredients: Chocolate pudding, gummy worms, crumbled chocolate wafer cookies
Directions: Fill a small bowl with chocolate pudding. Sprinkle the crumbled cookies over the chocolate mud. Push the gummy worms into the mud.

Enjoy!

Why don't you invent your own bug treat?

Unit 12

Goodbye school!

Hello summer!

My family is going to the cottage.

I will ride my bike every day.

I'm going to go swimming.

Up, Up and Away!

Warm-up

▶ **Describe the kites.**

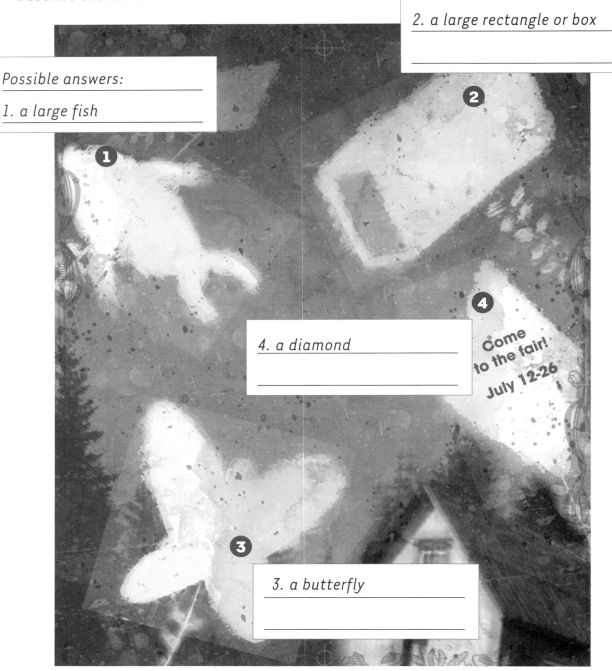

2. a large rectangle or box

Possible answers:

1. a large fish

4. a diamond

Come to the fair!
July 12-26

3. a butterfly

• **I shared my ideas with the class.**   Yes ☐   No ☐

Activity 1 A String of Kites

▶ Explain what each kite is for.

The girl's kite is for her mother / to welcome her mother home.

The boy's kite is for Children's Day / to celebrate Children's Day.

- I identified the purpose of each kite.   Yes ☐ No ☐
- I took notes as I listened to the recording.   Yes ☐ No ☐

Up, Up and Away!

Activity 2 Paper Magic

► Check off the material required for each kite.

Students will check off the material required for each kite.

Materials		
Carp kite	Paper	☑
	Paint or markers	☑
	String	☑
	Scrap paper	☑
	Glue	☑
	Straws	☐
Traditional kite	Paper	☑
	Paint or markers	☑
	String	☑
	Scrap paper	☑
	Glue	☑
	Straws	☑

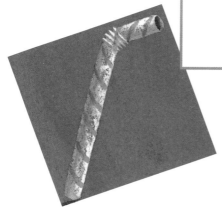

- I chose a _____ kite to make.
- It was easy ☐ difficult ☐ for me to make my kite.

116 one hundred and sixteen

Unit 12

Activity 3 Gone with the Wind

▶ **Write as many sentences as you can with the words listed in Table 1.**
▶ **Write your sentences in Table 2.**
▶ **Check off the answers that apply to you.**

Table 1

Column 1	Column 2	Column 3
I am going to	swim	my bike
I want to	ride	baseball
I will	visit	my skateboard
	eat	television
	play	the beach
	watch	the zoo
	sleep	ice cream

Table 2

Activities	I will do this activity this summer.	
	Yes	No
Answers will vary.		

• **I understood the messages on the kite tails.**
All of them ☐   Most of them ☐   Some of them ☐   None of them ☐
• **I wrote my own summer message.**
Yes ☐   No ☐

Extension Activity

Summer Wind

► **Write your summer activities on the kite tails.**

Answers will vary.

Activity 4 Poetry in Motion

▶ **Write a draft of your summer poem on the kite.**

Students will write a draft of their

summer poems.

- **I understood the poem "Summer's here!"** Yes ☐ No ☐
- **I wrote my own summer poem.** Yes ☐ No ☐
- **I used Chatterbox 12 for help.** Yes ☐ No ☐
- **I worked quietly.**
  Always ☐   Most of the time ☐   Some of the time ☐   Never ☐

Up, Up and Away!

Wrap-up

▶ **Plan your kite.**

Choose the materials you will use.

plastic sticks ☐
tissue paper ☐
styrofoam ☐
duct tape ☐
string ☐

straws ☐
wooden sticks ☐
fabric ☐
adhesive tape ☐
glue ☐

Draw a sketch of your kite.

Students will plan their kites.

• **I am satisfied with the kite I made.**
  Extremely ☐   Very ☐   Not very ☐   Not at all ☐

• **I checked my work carefully.**   Yes ☐   No ☐

Goodbye!

► **Plan a goodbye card.**
► **Write a message to your teacher or to a friend.**

Goodbye
Ms Boyer

I liked English.
It was fun.
Thank you.
Claude

Your message

Answers will vary.

Extra Activity

Souvenirs on the Wind

► Ask your school friends to write you a summer message.
► Collect their messages and signatures on the kite tails.

Answers will vary.